# Pokémon
## ADVENTURES
### X•Y

Story by
**Hidenori X**saka

Art by
**Satoshi Y**amamoto

**3**
VOLUME THREE

The Story Thus Far...

A story about young people entrusted with Pokédexes by the world's leading Pokémon researchers. Together with their Pokémon, they travel, do battle, and evolve!

**Y**

X's best friend in his group, and a Sky Trainer trainee. Her full name is Yvonne Gabena.

**X**

The main character of this chapter, and one of a close-knit group of five childhood friends. He was once a highly skilled Trainer who even won the Junior Pokémon Tournament, but now...

‹ **Kalos Region** ›

A star-shaped region filled with natural beauty. In the center of the region lies Lumiose City, a stone-paved city that is called the metropolis of art and artifice.

31333051178620

The Kalos region, Vaniville Town— four close childhood friends are trying to get the reclusive X out of his room when the legendary Pokémon Yveltal and Xerneas suddenly appear. The five friends are then attacked by a mysterious group wearing red suits who are trying to steal the Mega Ring that X wears on his arm like a bracelet. After escaping the attack, X and his friends embark on a journey to Lumiose City, where Professor Sycamore resides. They help Alexa, a journalist who is searching for the truth behind a series of strange occurrences, and continue to head west. But on the way, they are confronted by a Team Flare member who is gathering the Mega Stones! Manectric joins X's Pokémon team as they battle the Team Flare member in order to save their Mega Stone!

◄ Shauna ►

One of the five childhood friends. Her dream is to become a Furfrou Groomer. She is quick to speak her mind.

◄ Tierno ►

One of the five childhood friends. A big boy with an even bigger heart. He is currently training to become a dancer.

◄ Trevor ►

One of the five childhood friends. A quiet boy who hopes to become a Pokémon Researcher one day.

# The Mega Evolution Successors

A group of unique individuals based at the Tower of Mastery who have perfected the skill of Mega Evolution. When they find Trainers with potential, they perform a succession ceremony and bestow upon them an accessory equipped with a Key Stone for performing Mega Evolutions.

**Attacked** →

## Diantha
A famous actress from the Kalos region.

## Gurkinn
A pleasant elderly man known as the Mega Evolution Guru.

Grandfather →
← Granddaughter

## Korrina
The Shalour City Gym Leader. Good at roller-skating.

**Entrusts Mega Ring to**

## Alexa
A journalist at Lumiose Press.

Elder sister →
← Younger sister

## Viola
A photographer and the Santalune Gym Leader.

**The Five Friends of Vaniville Town**

 X

**Enemies** →

 Y
 Tierno
 Trevor
 Shauna

**Investigating the Vaniville Town Incident** ←

**Gym Leaders and Friends**

## Grant
An excellent rock climber and the Cyllage City Gym Leader.

Worries about ↓   Has respect for ↓

## Cassius
The keeper of the Kalos region Pokémon Storage System. An accommodating fellow who likes to Pokémon battle.

## Clemont
An inventor and the Lumiose City Gym Leader.

## Professor Sycamore
A Pokémon Researcher of the Kalos region. He entrusts his Pokémon and Pokédex to X and his friends.

**Assistants**

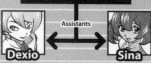

Dexio   Sina

## The Pokémon Storage System Group

# Character Connection Chart

Track the connections between the people revolving around X.

**Essentia**
A mysterious Trainer who wears an Expansion Suit.

## Team Flare

The devious members of this organization are identifiable by their red uniforms and have been wreaking havoc on the Kalos region. Their goal is to capture the legendary Pokémon Yveltal and Xerneas, and because of that their paths cross with X and his friends.

**Old friends**

**Lysandre**
The developer of the Holo Caster. He has a reputation for charitable acts but is also secretly the boss of Team Flare.

**Supports**

**Reports on his research**

### Team Flare's Scientific Team

**Xerosic**
Member of unit A. The only male member of the team, he is in charge of handling and developing Team Flare's gadgets.

**Celosia**
Member of unit A. A vengeful woman who somehow always bounces back from failure.

**Bryony**
Member of unit A. A quiet bookworm and military scientist who studies battles.

**Mable**
Member of unit B. Outspoken and emotional.

**Aliana**
Member of unit B. Charged with obtaining the Mega Ring.

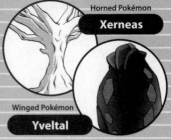

Horned Pokémon
**Xerneas**

Winged Pokémon
**Yveltal**

The two legendary Pokémon. They are currently disguised as a tree and a cocoon!

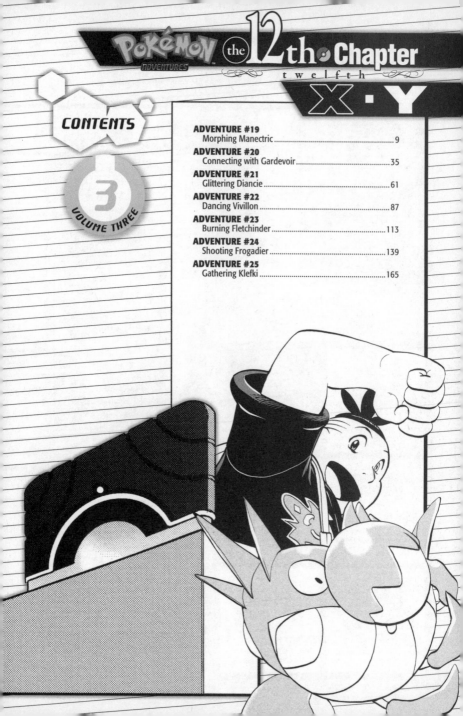

# POKÉMON ADVENTURES — the **12th** Chapter

twelfth

## X · Y

## CONTENTS

### VOLUME THREE — 3

**ADVENTURE #19**
Morphing Manectric ............................................................ 9

**ADVENTURE #20**
Connecting with Gardevoir .......................................... 35

**ADVENTURE #21**
Glittering Diancie ............................................................. 61

**ADVENTURE #22**
Dancing Vivillon .............................................................. 87

**ADVENTURE #23**
Burning Fletchinder ...................................................... 113

**ADVENTURE #24**
Shooting Frogadier ......................................................... 139

**ADVENTURE #25**
Gathering Klefki ............................................................. 165

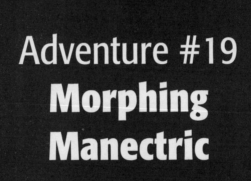

# Adventure #19
# **Morphing Manectric**

**X●Y**

WILD CHARGE!

OWWW...

RMBL

RMBL

RMBL

SHNKK

AAAH!

AIYEEE!

KRAK

BUT HIS POKÉMON RECEIVED RECOIL DAMAGE FROM THE ATTACK.

MANECTRIC SURROUNDED ITSELF WITH ELECTRICITY AND CHARGED MY TYRUNT...

WHAT A WASTE. WHO KNOWS HOW MUCH I COULD HAVE SOLD THIS FOR...

AFTER ALL, IT WAS POWERFUL ENOUGH TO BREAK THIS RESHIRAM STATUE!

WAIT...

KERRASSH

GRRR
!!

THAT WOULD HAVE BEEN A MUCH EASIER WAY TO GET INTO TEAM FLARE AND WEAR THIS UNIFORM...

WHY DIDN'T I SEE IT BEFORE? I WOULDN'T HAVE HAD TO WORK SO HARD IF I HAD JUST STOLEN THIS STATUE AND SOLD IT FOR THE FIVE MILLION I NEEDED TO JOIN!

NO MATTER HOW HARD I WORKED!

IF I WANTED TO LIVE IN A PALACE LIKE THIS, I'D NEVER BE ABLE TO!

THE GAP BETWEEN THE RICH AND THE POOR IS TOO GREAT! THE WORLD IS UNFAIR!

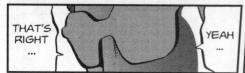

THAT'S RIGHT ...

YEAH ...

WE STEAL FROM THOSE WHO HAVE AND GIVE TO THOSE WHO DON'T. THAT'S THE RIGHT THING TO DO.

AND THAT'S WHY...

...WE STEAL!

SEE YOU AROUND!

NOW LET'S GO LOOK FOR THE OTHER MEGA STONES, TYRUNT!

ONCE AGAIN, ÉLEC!

IT'S NO USE!

ELEC-TRIC-TYPE ATTACKS AREN'T VERY EFFEC-TIVE AGAINST TYRUNT.

YOU MIGHT NOT HAVE NOTICED, BUT...

IT WON'T MAKE A BIT OF DIFFERENCE IF YOU ATTACK AT CLOSE RANGE.

SWFF

OH YEAH. IT'S OVER. LET'S CALL IT A DAY.

STEP

KA-THUNK

X ASKED ÉLEC TO USE THAT MOVE EVEN THOUGH HE KNEW THERE WOULD BE RECOIL DAMAGE...

...AND ÉLEC USED THE MOVE!

THAT MEANS THERE'S A BOND...

...BETWEEN THEM!

BUT YOU WOULD NEVER UNDERSTAND THAT BECAUSE ALL YOU CARE ABOUT IS MONEY!

...SO NAIVE I CAN'T STOP LAUGHING.

HWEEEE HWEEEE

YOU'RE SO NAIVE...

HAR HAR HAR!

HAR!

...

...YOU CAN BUY YOUR WAY **OUT OF** WITH MONEY.

OF COURSE THERE ARE THINGS YOU CAN'T BUY WITH MONEY. BUT THERE ARE EVEN MORE BAD THINGS...

EVEN SO, I CAN'T FORGIVE YOU FOR WHAT YOU JUST SAID.

CHEW THAT KID UP!

I WAS GOING TO LET YOU GO FREE, BUT I'VE CHANGED MY MIND!

AAAH!

I KNOW IT ISN'T LIKE ME TO TALK BACK LIKE THAT... BUT I GOT REALLY FRUSTRATED HEARING HIM SAY ALL THOSE THINGS!

THAT WAS A SURPRISE. I'VE NEVER SEEN YOU SO FIRED-UP BEFORE.

THANKS, X.

ARE YOU OKAY?

...WAS BE- CAUSE OF YOU.

THE REASON I WAS ABLE TO STAND UP FOR MYSELF...

THAT'S WHY I CONFRONTED HIM.

I WAS CONFIDENT YOU'D BE ABLE TO WIN.

WHAT...?

YOUR FLABÉBÉ IS THE KEY TO THIS BATTLE.

THAT'S NOT TRUE!

BUT THAT'S ALL I CAN DO. ME AND MY FLABÉBÉ CAN'T DO ANYTHING TO HELP YOU...

I DON'T KNOW...

MOM WAS WITH THE RED SUITS— WITH TEAM FLARE?! WHY?!

OOH, YOU'VE GOT QUITE A PARTY GOING ON HERE!

STRETTTCH!!

THREE.

YANK

AND ... ... FOUR!

TWO.

OH, COME ON.

For real.

LET'S GO BACK.

BO-RING.

HEY, CASSIUS! IS THAT ALL?

SQU EEZE

SHOOT!

WAIT! WE'RE JUST GETTING TO THE FUN PART...

I'VE CAPTURED ALL OF THEM EASILY.

...WHAT IT LOOKS LIKE BENEATH THEM.

THIS IS THE PERFECT OPPORTUNITY FOR ME TO SEE...

... EARS!

... ESPURR...

THERE'S SOMETHING I'VE ALWAYS WANTED TO FIND OUT...

HEY, HEY!!

?!

...LIKE MY AIPOM ARM.

MAYBE THEIR EARS WILL HELP ME COME UP WITH A NEW IDEA FOR AN INVENTION...

HUH? WHY NOT?

SHFF

DON'T LIFT ITS EAR UP!

ZZZZZZZ

RMMBL

RMMBL

RMMBL

RMMBL

EARTH-QUAKE!

HURRY UP AND STOP IT, TYRUNT!

WHAT A PAIN...

FWUMP

ADIEU!

HA HA HA... A SUPER EFFECTIVE MOVE! AND...YOUR POKÉMON HAS FAINTED. TOO BAD FOR YOU.

KRUNCH

WHY ?!

ZOOM

FLA-BÉBÉ!

WHOOAA!

RR

WHY, YOU ...!

SQUASH

...AND THAT HALVED THE POWER OF THE EARTH-QUAKE ATTACK!

YOU MUST HAVE USED GRASSY TERRAIN EARLIER ON...

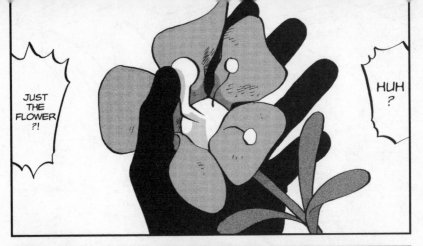

JUST THE FLOWER ?!

HUH ?

BOIN

RSTL RSTL

WHERE IS IT?!

HE DID IT!

HE GOT ME!

AIYEEE!

OH NO!

THUNDER-CLOUDS ARE QUICKLY GATHER-ING...!

FWUMP

MY STYLIN' UNIFORM!

AHH!

BOOM

WHO

...THE BOOT NOW IS...

THE ONLY WAY TO PREVENT TEAM FLARE FROM GIVING ME...

POINT

...TO CAPTURE MANECTRIC WITH THE MANECTITE AND TAKE IT TO XEROSIC!

LET'S SEE YOU TRY.

KERKRAKKK

SEE YOU AROUND!

OKAY.

MAYBE NOT TODAY...

OH ...UM...

HA HA HA HA HA...

WOM WOM WOM

SOUNDS RIGHT TO ME!

...A MEGA-MANECTRIC!

SO... I'M GUESSING ÉLEC'S MEGA-EVOLVED FORM WOULD BE...

AND LUCARIO MEGA EVOLVES INTO A MEGA LUCARIO.

A MEGA-EVOLVED KANGA IS A MEGA KANGASKHAN.

YEAH. HE MUST HAVE BEEN USING IT AS A GUIDE TO GATHER ALL THE MEGA STONES.

THE RED SUIT DROPPED THIS...?

PLUS, IT'S WRITTEN HERE.

...THIS IS A LIST OF MEGA STONES!

IN OTHER WORDS...

| | | | |
|---|---|---|---|
| | | | MEGA PINSIR |
| PINSIR | Ⓢ | PINSIRITE | MEGA MANECTRIC |
| MANECTRIC | Ⓢ | MANECTITE | MEGA KANGASKHAN |
| KANGASKHAN | Ⓢ | KANGASKHANITE | MEGA GYARADOS |
| GYARADOS | Ⓢ | GYARADOSITE | MEGA GARDEVOIR |
| GARDEVOIR | Ⓢ | GARDEVOIRITE | MEGA BANETTE |
| BANETTE | Ⓢ | BANETTITE | MEGA MEDICHAM |
| MEDICHAM | Ⓢ | MEDICHAMITE | MEGA SCIZOR |
| SCIZOR | Ⓢ | SCIZORITE | MEGA ALAKAZAM |
| ALAKAZAM | Ⓢ | ALAKAZITE | MEGA AERODA |
| AERODACTYL | Ⓢ | AERODACTYLITE | MEGA HERAC |
| HERACROSS | Ⓢ | HERACRONITE | MEGA HOUN |
| HOUNDOOM | Ⓢ | HOUNDOOMINITE | MEGA ABO |
| | | ABOMASITE | |

...EVERYTHING WILL BE **JUST PERFECT**— IF Y AND THE OTHERS ARE ALL RIGHT, THAT IS.

YES.

YOU EVEN FOUND A MEGA STONE LIST WE HAD NO IDEA EXISTED! AND NOW...

YOU MEGA EVOLVED MANEC-TRIC...

YOU GOT THE MEGA STONE BACK...

YOU'RE AMAZ-ING, X!

YEP. IT'S THE V.I.P. OF THIS BATTLE!

I HAVE TO LET MY FLABÉBÉ FIND A NEW FLOWER TOO.

TCH... I WARNED HIM NOT TO LIFT UP ESPURR'S EAR!

CLEMONT WAS BLOWN AWAY SOME-WHERE BY ESPURR'S PSYCHIC POWER?!

WHAT?!

I CAN HEAR YOU, YOU KNOW! For real.

UMM.

WHAT ARE **YOU** DOING IN THIS DUMP? AND WHO IS THAT SCARY-LOOKING PERSON?

I MAINTAIN THE KALOS REGION POKÉMON STORAGE SYSTEM.

For real.

I AM CASSIUS...

MY ASSISTANTS... OR FRIENDS... OR WHATEVER... HELP ME WITH MY WORK...

AND THESE GIRLS ...

HUH...? WHERE'S Y?

LOOK BEHIND YOU.

...THEY'RE ACTUALLY GOOD PEOPLE.

For real.

THEY LOOK A LITTLE SCARY AND UNSAVORY, BUT...

THAT'S HOW THEY ENDED UP HERE.

THEY'VE GOT NO DOUGH, NO FAMILY TO RELY ON, AND NO PLACE TO SLEEP.

...

YO.

HIYA.

HI.

HELLO.

WHAT ABOUT THE FOURTH ESPURR?

...THOSE THREE ESPURR BLASTED HIM AWAY!

CLEMONT SAW HER MOTHER, BUT BEFORE HE COULD TELL HER ANYTHING MORE ABOUT IT...

WHAT HAPPENED TO Y?!

HEY!

AND IT'S BEEN THERE EVER SINCE IT CAME TO.

THAT ONE STAYED BEHIND BECAUSE IT WAS CONFUSED.

...EMMA?

WHY DON'T YOU TAKE CARE OF IT...

## Current Location

### Parfum Palace

A luxurious palace constructed 300 years ago by a king who wished to display his power to all.

▼

### Camphrier Town

This ancient town was once famous for the long-neglected manor home of a noble family.

# Adventure #20
## Connecting with Gardevoir

**X Y**

A FEW YEARS AGO—

I FINALLY MADE IT UP HERE.

PHEW.

OH! HEY, LOOK OVER THERE!

WE'VE COME QUITE A LONG WAY, HUH.

YOU CAN DO IT.

COME ON.

TIRED, RIOLU?

I NEVER KNEW WE COULD SEE IT FROM SO FAR AWAY.

THAT'S THE SUNDIAL IN ANISTAR CITY. THEY SAY IT FELL FROM OUTER SPACE.

THE MEGA STONE ...... FOR YOU.

...NO MAT-TER WHAT !!

BUT I HAVE TO FIND IT TODAY...

IT'S ALREADY 8:00 P.M. IT'S GET-TING LATE.

UMM...

DO YOU SENSE SOME-THING THERE?

THE BUSH ON THE OTHER SIDE OF THE RIVER...

FWOOO

WHAT'S WRONG ?

BEHOLD! MEGA EVOLU- TION!!

WHAT IS IT? I'M JUST GETTING TO THE GOOD PART...

KOR- RINA.

KOR- RINA.

KOR- RINA.

OKAY, I'LL DO IT TOO...

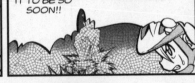

AH!!

GRAND-
FATHER?!

I KNEW THEY'D COME AFTER US, BUT I NEVER EXPECTED IT TO BE SO SOON!!

THE TOWER OF MASTERY WAS ATTACKED AND GRANDFATHER AND I ARE CURRENTLY ROAMING AROUND IN HIDING.

WHO ARE YOU?!

THE ENEMY?!

AS FOR YOUR GRAND-FATHER...

BUT I'M NOT ONE OF THEM!

YOU'RE NOT WRONG ABOUT THE ENEMIES.

A WOMAN?

HEEEY, KORRINA. YOU'VE WOKEN UP?

GRAND-FATHER!

UH-HUH! A DREAM OF MY SUCCESSION CEREMONY!

YOU SEEMED TO BE HAVING TROUBLE SLEEPING, BUT WERE YOU WATCHING A DREAM?

I SEE.

EVERYONE FROM THE FAMILY WAS THERE AND I COULD SEE THE FIREWORKS FROM PARFUM PALACE.

HI-YA-AH!!

IN THAT CASE...

THE ENEMY ATTACKED AFTER YOU FELL ASLEEP. THAT'S ALL.

THERE REALLY IS NOTHING TO IT.

YOU WANT ME TO EXPLAIN WHAT'S GOING ON, RIGHT?

GRANDFATHER... NOW ISN'T THE TIME TO TALK ABOUT THAT!!

BWOOOM

MEGA

KR AD OO M!!

...CHALM-ERS.

TEAM FLARE ADMIN...

SHA-LOUR CITY GYM LEAD-ER KOR-RINA.

IT'S JUST AS I HAVE HEARD.

HMM, YOUR FISTS ARE SO QUICK THAT YOU DON'T HAVE ANY TROUBLE DEALING WITH A LARGE GROUP.

WHO'S THERE?!

RMM MB
RR
LL LL

ONCE WE DRAG HIM INTO THE WATER, SKRELP WILL HAVE THE UPPER HAND.

SPLOOSH

GRAND-FATHER!!

...AND POISON HIM.

THEY WILL CAMOU-FLAGE THEM-SELVES AS ROTTEN KELP...

...WILL BE POISONED.

GURKINN AND HERA-CROSS...

THEN THE FAMOUS ACTRESS EVERYONE IS...

THAT'S RIGHT. THE SUCCESSOR WHO CAN MEGA EVOLVE HER GARDEVOIR...

...DIANTHA.

SLUDGE BOMB!!

BZZT

PSY-SHOCK!!

GO, DRAG-ALGE!!

54

RE-TREAT!!

R...

DIANTHA WON'T BE WITH US ALL THE TIME, YOU KNOW?

NOW, DON'T GET CARRIED AWAY, KORRINA.

WE'LL BE INVINCIBLE WITH THREE MEGA EVOLVED POKÉMON!

I'LL BE WITH YOU ALL THE WAY THROUGH.

NO.

DON'T WORRY ABOUT IT. I FINISHED MOST OF MY MAJOR WORK BEFOREHAND, SO I'VE GOT A BREAK FOR SOME TIME.

B-BUT WHAT ABOUT YOUR JOB AS AN ACTRESS?

OF COURSE. THAT'S WHY I CAME HERE.

R-REALLY?!

HMM...

AND WHAT DO THEY INTEND TO DO AFTER THEY GET HOLD OF IT?

...WHY THEY ARE AFTER IT?

THE ENEMY ARE CLEARLY AFTER THE MEGA EVOLUTION, BUT THE IMPORTANT THING IS...

YES.

IS THAT HOW YOU SEE THIS SITUATION?

KALOS IS IN CRISIS.

IS THERE ANOTHER ORGANIZATION WHO IS AFTER MEGA EVOLUTION...?

WHAT IS TEAM FLARE?

BUT BACK THEN...

THEY CALLED THEMSELVES "TEAM FLARE" TONIGHT...

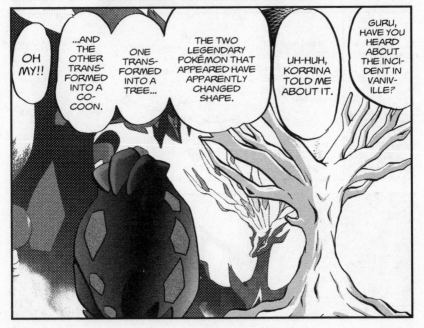

OH MY!!

...AND THE OTHER TRANSFORMED INTO A COCOON.

ONE TRANSFORMED INTO A TREE...

THE TWO LEGENDARY POKÉMON THAT APPEARED HAVE APPARENTLY CHANGED SHAPE.

UH-HUH, KORRINA TOLD ME ABOUT IT.

GURU, HAVE YOU HEARD ABOUT THE INCIDENT IN VANIVILLE?

...WE MUST FIND THE COCOON QUICKLY.

WHICH MEANS...

AND THE ENEMIES HAVE ALREADY DISCOVERED THE WHEREABOUTS OF THE TREE.

HOW ABOUT YOU?

I'VE PREPARED TO MAKE A CAPTURE.

KLAK

KLAK

RIGHT... I'VE FOUND A BEAUTIFUL ONE THAT WOULD SUIT THE BOSS PERFECTLY.

HELLO?

KLAK

WHAT?

SHF

I RESPECT YOUR KINDNESS BUT IT'S ONLY GOING TO LEAD TO A HUGE UNREDEEMABLE FAILURE ONE DAY.

YOU'RE SUCH A SOFTIE AS ALWAYS.

YOU ASSIGNED HIM TO THE NEXT MISSION?

AND CHALMERS?

WHAT? THEY FAILED AGAIN?

DIANTHA JOINED THEM?

TALK TO YOU LATER, XEROSIC.

OH, YOU'RE ON SOON.

I SEE. IS THAT SO. THAT'S WHY...

NEXT IS SHOW BIZ!!

## ON AIR

WE'RE BRINGING YOU THE LATEST NEWS TO ALL HOLO CASTER USERS.

THIS IS HER FIRST LONG BREAK SINCE HER DEBUT, SO I'M SURE THE ENTERTAIN-MENT REPORT-ERS WILL BE ALL OVER HER.

SHE SAYS SHE'LL BE TAKING A BREAK FOR A WHILE.

YESTERDAY, KALOS'S RENOWNED ACTRESS DIANTHA FINISHED FILMING HER LATEST MOVIE WHICH IS SCHEDULED TO COME OUT IN THE THEATERS NEXT SPRING!

OF COURSE, I, MALVA, WILL BE GOING AFTER HER TOO!

HMM, MAYBE SHE'S GOING ON VACATION?

## Current Location
(Korrina and others)

### Shalour City

The seaside home of the Tower of Mastery, where the legend of mysterious stones lives on.

▼

### Route 12
### Fourrage Road

Frolicking Skiddo can be seen and ridden at the Baa de Mer Ranch, located beside the breezy sea.

▼

### Coumarine City

An exclusive resort area made popular thanks to its clear skies and mild atmosphere.
*After arriving at Coumarine City, they moved along the coast to the northeast.

▼

### Route 14
### Laverre Nature Trail

The lush trees and boggy swamps of this trail give off an eerie vibe, even in broad daylight.

# Adventure #21
## Glittering Diancie

CAMPH-
RIER
TOWN

SHAB-
BONEAU
CASTLE

THE
BODY
GLOW-
ING IN
PINK.

JEWEL
POKÉMON
DIANCIE...

THE MOST
BEAUTIFUL
GLOW IN THE
WORLD.

NO, I JUST
WANT TO
TAKE ONE
LOOK AT IT!
DIANCIE!
DIANCIE!!

ROLL

ROLL

JUST FOR
ONCE,
I WANT
TO HOLD
DIANCIE
IN MY
HANDS...

SOO-
OOO
BEAUTI-
FUL...

BEAU-
TIFUL.
BEAU-
TIFUL.
OOH,
BEAUTI-
FUL.

AH!! I'M COUNTING ON YOU, MY FELLOW SERVANTS!

MASTER, WE'LL GO OUT TO SEARCH FOR DIANCIE AGAIN.

YES SIR!!

I HEAR THAT EVERY MILLIONAIRE IN THE WORLD IS SEARCHING FOR IT!!

YOU MUSTN'T FALL BEHIND ON THE SEARCH!!

RIGHT. YOU HAVE A FINE POSSIBILITY KORRINA.

RIGHT, DIANTHA?!

...I HAVE THE CHANCE OF BECOMING A CHAMPION TOO?

THEN, THEN...

I'VE HEARD OF A TRAINER IN A DIFFERENT REGION WHO WORKED AS A GYM LEADER FOR SEVERAL YEARS BEFORE BECOMING A CHAMPION.

HMM!

YOU PROTECT THE POKÉMON LEAGUE WITH THEM, SO YOU MUST GET ALONG WITH THEM!

HEY, WHAT ARE THE ELITE FOUR LIKE?!

YOU HAVE TO DEFEAT THE ELITE FOUR WHO ARE REALLY SKILLED TRAINERS.

BUT IT MUST BE HARD TO RISE UP TO BECOME THE CHAMPION.

...I GUESS YOU CAN SAY WE'RE GOOD FRIENDS.

WELL...

SIEBOLD IS ACTUALLY A TOP-CLASS CHEF WHO LOVES TO TREAT PEOPLE TO HIS FOOD.

THE WATER-TYPE GUY WITH A MENACING EXPRESSION.

DRASNA IS A FRIENDLY WOMAN WHO IS ALWAYS SMILING.

THE DRAGON-TYPE LADY!

WIKSTROM. HE'S A CALM MAN BUT HE CAN BE A BIT STUBBORN.

HOW'S THE STEEL-TYPE TRAINER IN ARMOR?

WELL... SHE'S...

MALVA, HUH.

WOW, THEY'RE ALL SO DIFFERENT.

AND WHAT ABOUT THE NEWS REPORTER?

A FIERY WOMAN.

AND...SHE KEEPS THAT FIRE HIDDEN... INSIDE HER TOO.

HA HA HA.

I'M A FAILURE AS AN ACTRESS.

WHY?

YOU LOOKED A LITTLE DEPRESSED.

WHAT?!

DON'T YOU LIKE HER?

ONE REASON IS BECAUSE SHE'S A VERY BUSY PERSON...

...BUT I'VE NEVER BEEN ABLE TO FATHOM HER.

...BUT I HAVE NEVER DONE ANY OF THAT WITH MALVA.

IT'S NOT THAT WE DON'T GET ALONG...

I'VE FOUGHT AGAINST THE OTHER THREE BEFORE AND I'VE MET THEM IN PRIVATE TOO...

65

SHFF    SHFF    SHFF

SHFF SHFF

OKAY!

WELL THEN! WE'VE FINISHED EATING, SO LET'S GO AND HELP THE GURU.

MAYBE THEY MET A WILD POKÉMON THEY DON'T LIKE?

THEY SEEM TO BE RUNNING AWAY IN A HURRY...

CAR-BINK...

NO, I'M FINE.

NEED ANY HELP, GRAND-FA-THER?!

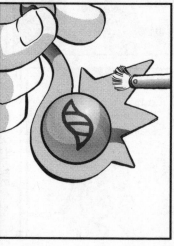

66

I'VE WASHED OFF THE SLUDGE FROM THE SWAMP AND ALL I NEED TO DO NOW IS TO CHECK THE KEY STONES.

THE KEY STONES EMBEDDED IN THEM STILL RETAIN A VERY HIGH PURITY.

KORRINA AND MY MEGA GLOVES AND DIANTHA'S MEGA CHARM.

...CAN'T YOU JUST GIVE THE KEY STONE TO THE TRAINER AS IT IS, OR EMBED ALL OF THEM IN THE SAME KIND OF ACCESSORY?

HEY, GRANDFATHER.

I'VE ALWAYS WANTED TO ASK YOU BUT...

...BUT THE MOST IMPORTANT THING IS ITS DEGREE OF PURITY.

I HAVE CREATED MANY ACCESSORIES INCLUDING THE MEGA RING...

THE KEY STONE...IS A STONE THAT WILL DRAW OUT WHAT IS INSIDE THAT TRAINER.

THAT'S GOOD.

YOU'VE STARTED TO USE YOUR IMAGINATION.

HA HA HA.

IT NEEDS TO BE WORN IN A WAY THAT WILL FIT THAT TRAINER.

THAT IS WHY I WILL DECIDE ON THE SHAPE OF THE ACCESSORY AFTER GETTING TO KNOW THAT PERSON.

...POKÉMON THAT HAVE THE POSSIBILITY OF MEGA EVOLVING OFTEN BECOME A TARGET.

AND... BECAUSE OF THAT MYSTERY...

THAT'S RIGHT. THAT IS THE MYSTERY OF THE MEGA EVOLUTION.

WHAT A STRANGE STONE.

HMM.

AND... THERE'S ANOTHER POKÉMON OF THAT NATURE HERE TOO...

...AND IT LOOKED AS IF THEY WERE...

HMM, HMM.

I SAW A GROUP OF CARBINK OVER THERE...

MAYBE THE CARBINK I SAW ESCAPED FROM HERE.

OH MY! THERE'S A CAVE HERE...

HUH? WHAT DO YOU MEAN?

COULD YOU HELP ME?

YOU TWO.

IS SOMETHING BOTHERING YOU?

HMM.

...IT'S MORE LIKE AN ENTRANCE THAT GOES DOWN TO A HIGH TEMPERATURE UNDERGROUND LOCATION...

RIGHT. THIS ISN'T A CAVE...

WHAT A STEEP SLOPE!

OF COURSE, WE NEED TO HURRY WITH THE COCOON TOO, BUT...

TO BE HONEST, I DECIDED TO CAMP OUT HERE BECAUSE I WAS WORRIED ABOUT THIS CAVE.

HOW AWFUL!!

AND SO MANY OF THEM TOO!

CARBINK!!

HMM! JUST AS I THOUGHT!!

CARBINK ARE A JEWEL POKÉMON.

WHY WOULD ANYONE DO THIS?!

69

WRONG.

IN OTHER WORDS, IT'S FOR MONEY.

IF YOU POLISH THEIR BODIES, YOU CAN SELL THEM FOR A HIGH PRICE.

YOU ATTACKED THE CARBINK TO LURE OUT DIANCIE THAT LIVED WITH THEM!!

...SO YOU KNOW ABOUT THE PINK PRINCESS.

HMM...

DIAN-CIE...

MY CLIENT TOLD ME, "WE'LL PAY YOU ANY SUM OF MONEY YOU WANT IF YOU CAPTURE DIANCIE."

RIGHT.

I'M A JEWEL THIEF, YOU SEE.

...AND FOUND OUT ABOUT THIS CAVE WHILE I PRETENDED TO BE HIS SERVANT.

SO I APPROACHED AN IMPOVER-ISHED NOBLE WHO HAD THE DOCUMENTS ON DIANCIE...

THEY LIVE IN A CAVE AC-COMPANIED BY A LARGE GROUP OF CARBINK AND ARE KNOWN AS THE ROYAL PINK PRINCESS FROM THEIR BEAUTIFUL GLOWING PINK COLOR.

DIANCIE IS A MUTATED CARBINK.

SO THE DOCUMENTS AT THE TOWER OF MASTERY WEREN'T THE ONLY DOCU-MENTS LEFT ON IT, HUH.

THAT'S RIGHT.

GRAND-FATHER!! PINK PRINCESS AS IN THE POKÉMON YOU WERE TALKING ABOUT WHEN WE LEFT THE TOWER OF MASTERY ...?

ITS NAME IS DIAN-CIE.

...WAY!! ...O... N...

WOULD YOU BE SO KIND AS TO LET ME PASS?

SO, I MUST DELIVER DIANCIE TO MY CLIENT.

GO, BINA-CLE!!

IF YOU WANT TO FIGHT!!

SHA

CHOOM

CHOOM

CHOO

CHOOM

THE GURU MUST HAVE A PLAN. LET'S PRETEND TO HAVE BEEN DEFEATED AND LET THEM GO OUT.

HUUH?! WHY?!

DIANTHA, KORRINA WE'RE GOING TO LET THEM OUT OF THE CAVE FIRST.

TWO HEADS ON ONE ROCK! IT FEELS LIKE I'M FIGHTING AGAINST SIX POKÉMON AT ONCE!!

He got us!

HA HA HA! EXCUSE ME!!

BE-HOLD!!

...AND THE LIGHT OF THE MEGA STONE— MERGE!!

THE LIGHT OF MY KEY STONE...

OKAY, LET'S GO AFTER HIM!!

MEGA EVO- LU- TION !!

WHOA, WHOA, WHOA !!

WHOA...

BLAM

BOO SH

YES, SIR!

REMEMBER! LURE THEM OUT TO THE TOP OF THE HILL!

KRRCH

Huff

KRRCH

Huff

LOOK.

KWEEE
E

ACK.

KOFF.

WELL, SORRY TO BE IMPOV- ERISHED.

THERE WAS NOTHING ON IT IN THAT IMPOV- ERISHED NOBLE'S DOCU- MENTS!!

I-I DIDN'T KNOW IT COULD USE A MOVE LIKE THIS...

MOON-BLAST.

AN ATTACK THAT USES THE POWER OF THE MOON.

FW U M P

EVER SINCE I HIRED YOU, DOCUMENTS WENT MISSING AND YOU'D RUN OFF ON YOUR OWN WHEN I ASKED EVERYONE TO LOOK FOR DIANCIE. AND ON TOP OF THAT YOU WERE CONTACTING SKETCHY PEOPLE, TOO.

I ALWAYS KNEW SOMETHING WAS GOING ON.

MAS-TER!!

SO I FOLLOWED YOU HERE...AND JUST AS I THOUGHT!! YOU WERE PLANNING ON STEALING DIANCIE FROM ME FROM THE START, RIGHT?!

ACK...

AND ON TOP OF THAT, I'M TURNING YOU IN TO THE POLICE!!

YOU'RE FIRED!!

AW NO!

I BET YOU WERE BEING SO BLATANT, THINKING, "HE'S JUST AN IMPOVERISHED NOBLE, HE'D NEVER NOTICE," RIGHT?!

PTOOEY PTOOEY

Eww!

MASTER, THAT'S ENOUGH.

I KNE-EE-EW IT!!

THAT MAN SAID HE WAS LOOKING FOR DIANCIE FOR A CLIENT WHO'D PAY HIM A HANDSOME SUM.

FWO

BINACLE! THE MOON IS HIDDEN BY THE CLOUDS! DON'T LET DIANCIE GO!!

WHAT?!

YOU WERE SO DESPERATE TO SEE DIANCIE AND I FOUND IT FOR YOU!

YOU SHOULD BE THANKING ME.

THAT'S CALLED DIAMOND STORM.

OOH! WHAT A BEAUTIFUL MOVE!!

OW-WWW.

THUDD THUDD

YOU CAN USE IT TO ATTACK AND DEFEND YOURSELF AT ONCE, HUH.

THIS IS AN ATTACK MOVE THAT MAKES USE OF THAT.

DIANCIE HAS THE POWER TO CONDENSE THE CARBON IN THE ATMOSPHERE TO CREATE DIAMONDS.

RATATATA
TAT!!ATATA

AIYEEEE!!

BULLET SEED.

YOUR BINACLE HAVE ALL FAINTED. DO YOU STILL WANT TO FIGHT? OR WILL YOU GO TO THE POLICE?

...EITH-ER OF THEM!!

I WON'T CHOOSE...

LADY MALVA!!

ZSH

LOOKS LIKE YOU FAILED.

Huff

Gasp

CLOMP

Huff

CLOMP

Gasp

DIANCIE CREATED THEM. IT'S NOT MUCH OF A SUBSTITUTE FOR DIANCIE BUT PLEASE ACCEPT THEM.

WHAT ARE THESE?

WHAT LARGE, BEAUTIFUL DIAMONDS.

...PLEASE TAKE THESE!

I'M SORRY!! BUT...

Phew...

I'LL TAKE THEM.

HOW'S THIS...

RIGHT.

IN THAT CASE, COULD YOU PAY ME...? AND PREFERABLY FOR THE DIAMONDS I GAVE YOU TOO, SINCE I PRACTICALLY MADE DIANCIE CREATE THEM...

UM... IS THAT ALL FOR THIS MISSION?

...FOR YOUR PAY-MENT?

KRSHAA!

HUMPH... IT'S ALWAYS THE USELESS PEOPLE WHO ARE SHAMELESS ENOUGH TO ASK FOR REWARDS...

WHOOOAAA!!

...SO I'LL CALL IT EVEN.

BUT I'VE GOTTEN HOLD OF SO MANY BEAUTIFUL DIAMONDS...

I WILL DESTROY ALL THE DOCUMENTS I HAVE SO THE BAD PEOPLE WON'T TAKE ADVANTAGE OF ME AND WILL NEVER LOOK FOR DIANCIE AGAIN!

IF YOU COULD DO THAT, DIANCIE WILL BE HAPPY TOO.

I HAVE NO REGRETS.

I EVEN MANAGED TO SEE BEAUTIFUL MOVES LIKE MOONBLAST AND DIAMOND STORM.

OOOOOH, HOOOOW BEAUTIFUL.

LET'S GO BACK TO SHAB-BONEAU CASTLE!

VROOM

WELL THEN!

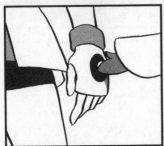

WHAT'S THE MEANING OF THIS, GRAND-FATHER ?!

...IS A POKÉ-MON THAT CAN MEGA EVOLVE TOO.

DIAN-CIE...

WHAT ?!

PEOPLE WHO ARE AFTER DIANCIE FOR ITS MONETARY VALUE AND BEAUTY AREN'T MUCH OF A THREAT.

I WAS WORRIED ABOUT THOSE WHO WERE AFTER ITS POWER.

IT WOULD PROBABLY BE BETTER FOR IT TO MOVE TO A DIFFERENT LOCATION ALONG WITH THE CARBINK.

HOWEVER, ITS SAFE REFUGE HAS BEEN DISCOVERED.

...THE ROYAL PINK PRINCESS.

FAREWELL, DIANCIE...

HNGH...

...I CANNOT FORCE MYSELF AS MUCH AS I USED TO.

LOOKS LIKE...

...ARE ERODING MY BODY AWAY.

THE INJURY I RECEIVED AT THE TOWER AND THE POISON FROM SKRELP AT THE SWAMP...

...AND GET THROWN INTO A HOSPITAL.

BUT I CANNOT LET THEM FIND OUT...

...TO PROPERLY SUCCEED THE POWER OF MEGA EVOLUTION TO HIM...

I MUST MEET HIM AS SOON AS POSSIBLE...

## Current Location

**Camphrier Town**

This ancient town was once famous for the long-neglected manor home of a noble family.

▼

**Route 7**
**Rivière Walk**

The longest single road in the Kalos region runs straight alongside one of its greatest rivers.

▼

Battle Chateau

Adventure #22
**Dancing Vivillon**

X•Y

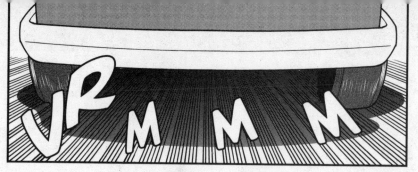

THANK YOU.

THE BATTLE CHATEAU IS REALLY IMPRESSIVE...

I'M SO GLAD YOU'RE HERE.

I'M HERE TO DO MAINTENANCE ON YOUR POKÉMON STORAGE SYSTEM.

HIYA, I'M CASSIUS.

IT'S THEIR OWN FAULT IF THEY LEAVE THEIR VALUABLES LYING AROUND.

AND DON'T STEAL ANYTHING, OKAY?

...

OKAY, OKAY! I'LL DO MY BEST.

I'LL TRY NOT TO.

YEP.

GO ON INSIDE AND DO THE SYSTEM CHECK FOR ME.

OKAY, THANKS.

I'LL GO HELP THEM.

MIMI, HUH...?

ITS NAME IS MIMI.

HEY, EMMA! THAT ESPURR SEEMS TO REALLY LIKE YOU.

YOU CAN COME OUT.

THE COAST IS CLEAR.

SLAM

NOW...

KLIK

PHEEEW!

BUT DON'T GET OUT OF THE CAR! For real.

...WHILE I WORK ON THIS JOB.

TAKE A BREAK AND STRETCH A LITTLE...

SORRY IT WAS SO CRAMPED IN THERE... AND YOU'VE STILL GOT QUITE A DISTANCE TO GO BEFORE YOU REACH CYLLAGE CITY.

PHEEEW.

WOW, I'M POOPED.

HMM...

THEN AGAIN, I'M NOTHING SPECIAL...

For real.

HA HA HA! I AM MOST DEFINITELY A NICE PERSON.

I'VE GOT ANOTHER CALL TO GO TO TODAY RIGHT AFTER THIS.

For real.

...YOU GET CALLS FROM ALL OVER KALOS ASKING YOU TO FIX THIS OR THAT DEVICE.

For real.

WHEN YOU'RE TECH SUPPORT FOR THE STORAGE SYSTEM...

IT'S AN OLD RATTLE-TRAP THOUGH, SO DON'T EXPECT A LUXURY CRUISE.

YOU'RE WELCOME TO RIDE IN OUR VEHICLE WITH US.

WE TOLD HIM ABOUT THE PEOPLE WHO'VE BEEN ATTACKING US, AND HE OFFERED TO HELP US TRAVEL INCOGNITO.

HE JOKES AROUND A LOT, BUT IT SEEMS LIKE WE CAN TRUST HIM...

THE FIVE DON'TS

I GUESS Y HAS BEEN...

I KNOW. NO MATTER WHAT WE'VE GONE THROUGH, SHE WAS ALWAYS OUR LEADER.

...THAN WE REALIZED OVER HER MOTHER.

...A LOT MORE TORN UP...

HE'S GONE!

X?

COULD HE BE...?!

WHERE'S X-EY?

HUH?

WHAT IS HE DOING?!

DIDN'T I TELL YOU TO STAY INSIDE THE CAR?

HEY!

GRRR...

WHY SHOULD I TAKE ORDERS FROM YOU?

YANK

BON

YEAH, OKAY. YOU'VE GOT A POINT THERE. BUT...

KVCK

AND I CAN'T LET YOU INTERFERE WITH THE SEARCH FOR YOUR GIRLFRIEND'S MOM. For real.

I'VE GOT PLANS OF MY OWN.

JUG JUG

WHAT ARE YOU DOING, TREVOR?!

SORRY, CAS-SIUS!

SHOOT!

SHF

DON'T ROCK THE BOAT! WE'RE DEPENDENT ON THIS GUY FOR A RIDE!

SHH!

TREVOR...!

X WANTS TO BECOME STRONGER TO PROTECT US, SO HE CAN'T STAY INSIDE THE VAN ALL THE TIME.

HE NEEDS TO HAVE PRACTICE BATTLES WITH IT.

THIS MANEC-TRIC, ÉLEC, IS X'S NEW POKÉ-MON.

AND TO DO THAT WE NEED CAS-SIUS'S HELP.

WE HAVE TO GET TO CYLLAGE CITY AS FAST AS WE CAN FOR Y'S SAKE.

AREN'T YOU A LITTLE TOO TRUSTING OF THESE GROWN-UPS?

PROFESSOR SYCAMORE... AND NOW THIS GUY...

HEY, TREVOR...

SCHLOOP

I HAVEN'T BEEN ABLE TO CLOSE THE DISTANCE BETWEEN US YET.

...

NO PROBLEM. I'M USED TO IT.

SORRY, CASSIUS!

SLAM

...UNITE THE FIVE OF US...

I KNEW IT. ONLY Y CAN...

THP

HEY!

WHAT HAP-PENED TO THEM?

...A LOT OF TOWNSPEOPLE AND POKÉMON WENT MISSING.

...WHEN YVELTAL AND XERNEAS FOUGHT EACH OTHER AT VANIVILLE TOWN...

THAT DAY...

...SO WE CAP-TURED THEM.

IT WOULD HAVE BEEN A PITY TO WASTE ALL THOSE RE-SOURC-ES...

THERE'S ONE WOMAN WHO KEEPS TRYING TO ESCAPE, SO I RAISED THE SECURITY LEVEL ON HER.

AND I'VE PLACED ALL THE POKÉMON INSIDE A SPECIAL POKÉ BALL.

THE TOWNS-PEOPLE ARE ALL IN THE DUNGEON HERE...

WE DON'T HAVE ENOUGH GRUNTS TO MOVE IT.

I GOT PERMISSION FROM THE BOSS TO TRANSPORT THE BIG TREE.

...WHAT ARE YOU GOING TO DO WITH THESE PEOPLE?

AND I...

I SEE.

I'M SO, SO SORRY!!

...YOU ALSO LET THE ENEMY GET AHOLD OF THE LIST!

...NOT ONLY HAVE YOU FAILED...

THE BOSS OR-DERED YOU TO COLLECT THE MEGA STONES, BUT...

SO IT WAS YOU, HUH?

I GUESS ALL THOSE HOSTAGES ARE STRONGER THAN A FEW GRUNTS.

OH, I SEE.

BUT I WILL FORGIVE YOU... FOR TWO REASONS.

YOU CAN'T ERASE YOUR FAIL-URES.

OUR BOSS IS USING IT, BUT YOU'RE THE ONE WHO FOUND IT, RIGHT?

FIRST, THE GYARA-DOSITE.

THANK YOU, THANK YOU!

LUCKY FOR YOU, YOU LEFT THE ESPURR AT THE SCENE OF THE BATTLE. THAT'S HOW WE MANAGED TO CAPTURE HIM.

AND SECONDLY... BECAUSE OF HIM.

LIKE I SAID... YOU'RE LUCKY.

I'LL BE TAKING SOME OF THE CAPTURED TOWNS-PEOPLE WITH ME.

I'LL NEED SOME SOL-DIERS.

I'M LIS-TEN-ING.

XERO-SIC...

WHAT'S THIS?

OH?

AND THE POKÉMON TOO.

I'M MOVING UP IN THE RANKS, YOU KNOW!

WHAT ?!

I WANT IT BACK.

I LENT YOU MY PYROAR, BUT I HEARD THAT YOU HAVEN'T BEEN ABLE TO MAKE GOOD USE OF IT.

I'LL TAKE THIS.

NICE.

**S M A S H**

MUMBL MUMBL MUMBL

**KLTTR**

YES ?

OH, AND ALIANA ...?

105

I'M THE ONE WHO STANDS BEHIND THE BOSS.

I HAVE TO LOOK GOOD.

KLCK

WHAT ABOUT YOUR ASSISTANTS?

THEY'RE WAITING IN THE BACKYARD.

LET'S GO.

SORRY TO KEEP YOU WAITING.

NOW THE RANKED TRAINERS WHO VISIT THE BATTLE CHATEAU WILL BE ABLE TO MOVE THE TRAYS AND USE THE BATTLE BOX WITH EASE.

NO NEED TO THANK ME. I'M ONLY DOING MY JOB.

THANKS FOR ALL YOUR HARD WORK, CASSIUS.

YOU'RE FREE TO USE IT AS YOU WISH.

AND I CAN USE THAT, RIGHT ...?

OKAY, OUT YOU GO.

KRRK

OWWW.

ARE YOU SURE ABOUT THIS, TREVS? WHAT'S HAPPENING?

WHAT A
SURPRISE!
WHY
DID YOU
CHANGE
FROM
LAND TO
AIR?!

ZOOOOP

WHUPPA

WHUPPA

WHUPPA

IT'S A PITCH-BLACK CAVE INFESTED WITH ZUBAT. YOU WOULDN'T WANT TO DEAL WITH THAT, WOULD YOU? For real.

IF I DIDN'T, YOU'D HAVE TO GO THROUGH A PLACE CALLED THE CONNECTING CAVE TO GET TO CYLLAGE CITY.

...IT'S BEST TO AVOID THE CAVE.

SO...

....!

BUT THE MAIN PROBLEM IS THAT IT WOULD BE THE PERFECT PLACE FOR AN AMBUSH BY THOSE PEOPLE WHO ARE AFTER YOU. For real.

IT'S A SCARY PLACE...

HE'S THE GYM LEADER OF LUMIOSE CITY! For real.

I SHOULD HAVE REMEMBERED EARLIER...

THE NAME CLEM-ONT... AND HIS SO-CALLED STATUS AS KALOS'S GREAT-EST INVENT-OR...

I RE-CALLED SOME-THING ABOUT FOUR EYES TOO...

COME TO THINK OF IT, ÉLEC CAME FROM PRISM TOWER, RIGHT...?

MAYBE THAT'S WHY HE WAS VISITING CYLLAGE.

BUT THE BLACK-OUT HAS BEEN CAUSING A LOT OF PROB-LEMS LATELY.

THE PRISM TOWER IS ALSO A POKÉ-MON GYM.

109

I HOPE HE'S ALL RIGHT.

THEN YOU MUST BE WORRIED ABOUT HIM.

YOU KNOW CLE-MONT ?!

WHAT IS IT?

HMM ...

AGH! THERE'S EVEN MORE THAN THAT!

TEN... NO, FIF-TEEN ?!

AND IT'S HEADING STRAIGHT FOR US!

SOME-THING ON THE RADAR.

SWISH

THAT MEANS THEY MUST BE...

IT'S THE SAME FLYING SUIT AS Y-EY'S!

THAT SHAD-OW!

...SKY TRAINERS?!

## Current Location

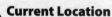

**Route 7**
**Rivière Walk**

The longest single road in the Kalos region runs straight alongside one of its greatest rivers.

**Battle Chateau**

**Above the Connecting Cave**

This cave linking Route 7 and Cyllage City is notable for its great hordes of Zubat.
\* They used an air route to avoid the cave.

# Adventure #23
# Burning Fletchinder

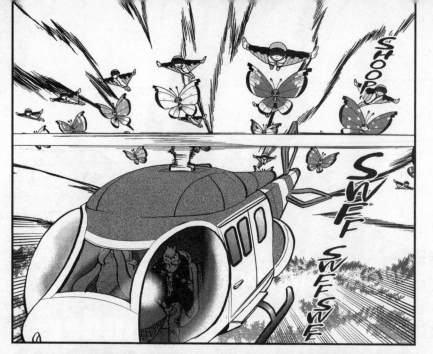

WE'RE GONNA CRASH!

SWFFZZZZT

TH UN TAT K

When did you have time to count them?!

FIFTEEN OF THEM USED HURRICANE AT THE SAME TIME! IMPRESSIVE TEAMWORK. IT'S A MIRACLE WE DIDN'T CRASH.

PHEW! THAT WAS CLOSE ...! For real.

I'M LUCKY AND TALENTED, BUT ANOTHER ONE OF THOSE ATTACKS AND EVEN I WON'T BE ABLE TO PREVENT US FROM CRASH-ING...

THEY'RE AT-TACK-ING AGAIN!

NOK

WHA ....?!

GRIN

IT'S MORSE CODE. WE STUDY IT AT THE SKY TRAINER TRAINING SCHOOL.

37

NOK

NOK

W-WHAT'S SHE DOING? For real.

NOK

NOK NOK

NOK NOK

"YOU'RE BETTER OFF ON THE GROUND" ...

... she's saying.

"I'LL KNOCK YOU DOWN.

"COME OUT, YVONNE GABENA."

THAT'S WHAT SHE'S SAYING.

GO AHEAD.

CASSIUS, MAY I OPEN THE HATCH?

Y!

**SHFF**

I AM. BUT...

ARE YOU SURE YOU'RE UP FOR THIS? YOU'RE STILL UPSET ABOUT GRACE—YOUR MOM!

I'M GOING OUT TO HAVE A SKY BATTLE.

Y!

Y-EY, WHAT ARE YOU DOING ?!

...REGRETTING WHAT I **DIDN'T** DO IN THE PAST. IT'S ABOUT TIME I DID **SOMETHING** IN THE **PRESENT**!

...THINGS WON'T GET BETTER IF I KEEP HIDING UNDER A BLANKET...

LET'S GO, FLET-CHY!

...

I HEARD A LOT OF STUDENTS ARE STILL MISSING.

THE SCHOOL WAS BLOWN OFF THE MAP...

YES.

SKY TRAINER TRAINING SCHOOL... AS IN... THE ONE AT VANIVILLE TOWN?

I KNOW IT'S YOU.

AND A TRULY IMPRESSIVE FLIGHT FORMATION...

VIVILLON FROM AROUND THE WORLD...

IT'S YOU, ISN'T IT, YVETTE?

I WAS WORRIED YOU'D FORGOTTEN ME.

OH, YOU REMEMBERED!

...YVONNE GABENA!

SKY TRAINER TRAINING SCHOOL

OF COURSE I WOULD NEVER FORGET— OR FORGIVE— YOU...

WHY IS IT ALWAYS HER...

WHY IS IT ALWAYS HER...

OR ELSE THEIR HURRICANE WILL DRAG THE HELICOPTER IN AND ENDANGER X AND THE OTHERS!

I HAVE TO MOVE FAR-THER AWAY!

ACK ...!

YOU'RE RUN-NING AWAY AGAIN ?!

THE VIVILLON ALL BELONG TO YVETTE, SO THEIR FORMATION WILL FALL APART THE MOMENT I DEFEAT HER.

THE OTHER FOURTEEN MUST BE YVETTE'S GROUPIES.

IF ONLY WE COULD DO SOME-THING TO HELP HER ...!

SHE'S MOVING AWAY SO SHE WON'T DRAG US INTO THE BATTLE...!

Y!

TREVOR... OUR JOB ISN'T TO HELP WITH HER SKY BATTLE.

IT'S TO FIND THE "EYE."

OUR JOB IS TO LOOK FOR IT.

IT HAS TO BE SOMEWHERE AROUND HERE.

YOU OUGHT TO REMEMBER THAT, SHAUNA.

THE... EYE?

STILL, YOU ALWAYS GET ALL THE ATTENTION! BUT WHY?!

ON TOP OF THAT YOU ONLY HAVE A FLETCHLING, WHICH CAN'T PARTICIPATE IN A SKY BATTLE.

NOW YOU CAN'T FLY AS FAST BECAUSE YOU'RE GETTING AIR RESISTANCE.

DIDN'T YOU LEARN AT SCHOOL THAT WE HAVE TO DRESS CAREFULLY, EVEN THOUGH IT TAKES TIME?

YOU PUT IT ON IN A HURRY, HUH?

YOUR WING SUIT HAS AIR IN IT.

I FINALLY SAID IT.

PHEW.

ACK...!

SERIOUSLY, I WISH THE TEACHERS WOULD STOP MAKING A FUSS OVER ME.

...BUT THE OTHER STUDENTS RESENT ME FOR THE SAME REASON.

THE TEACHERS TREAT ME LIKE I'M SPECIAL BECAUSE MY MOTHER'S FAMOUS...

YOU HAVE NO IDEA HOW TOUGH IT IS TO BE THE DAUGHTER OF A CELEBRITY.

TRMBL

SHE'D PROBABLY JUST SAY, "SEE? I TOLD YOU NOT TO TRY TO BE A SKY TRAINER!"

I CAN'T EVEN TALK TO MY MOTHER ABOUT IT...

TRMBL

SO IN THE END...

I CHOSE TO TRAIN AS A SKY TRAINER BECAUSE I WANT TO DISTINGUISH MYSELF FROM MY FAMOUS MOTHER...

WOM WOM

AT LEAST, THAT'S WHAT I USED TO THINK...

...EVERYTHING IS ALL HER FAULT!

WOM

131

I CAN'T BELIEVE I GOT SO DEPRESSED THAT I WOULDN'T EVEN TALK TO MY FRIENDS ABOUT MY PROBLEMS.

AND I'M WORRIED ABOUT HER.

...I REALLY MISS HER.

BUT NOW THAT MY MOTHER HAS DISAPPEARED...

THANK YOU.

...FOR GIVING ME THIS OPPORTUNITY TO VENT.

YOU KNOW, I SHOULD BE GRATEFUL TO YOU, YVETTE...

THAT'S RIGHT. AND COME TO THINK OF IT, IT DIDN'T MAKE SENSE...

IT WAS CONTROLLING ALL THE SKY TRAINERS!

THE POKÉMON WHO CAN CONTROL PEOPLE'S MINDS— AEGISLASH.

IT'S THE SAME POKÉMON THAT WAS CONTROLLING SHAUNA.

WHERE HAVE THEY BEEN SINCE THEY DISAPPEARED?

WHY ELSE WOULD YVETTE AND ALL HER GROUPIES TURN ON Y ALL OF A SUDDEN?

I THINK WE'RE ABOUT TO FIND OUT...

AND WHAT HAPPENED TO THE PEOPLE OF VANIVILLE TOWN AFTER THE ATTACK?

136

THERE IT IS— CYLLAGE CITY.

...MY GIRL-FRIEND!

SQUISH

SHE'S NOT ...

HUH?

I HOPE YOU FIND YOUR GIRL-FRIEND'S MOM.

I MEAN IT!

For real.

HA HA... OKAY. IF YOU SAY SO.

For real.

## Current Location

**Route 8**
**Above Muraille Coast**

This is a road of great contrasts,
from the harsh rock of the cliffs to
the soft sands of the beach.
* They're taking the air route.

# Adventure #24
## Shooting Frogadier

**X Y**

SW FF SW FF

I'M NOT SO SURE ABOUT THAT ...

NOW WE CAN GET TO CYLLAGE CITY SAFELY.

HOW NICE OF THEM! THEY WEREN'T EVEN ORDERED TO HELP THEM!

THE VIVILLON HELPED ALL THE MIND-CONTROLLED SKY TRAINERS...

IT WON'T FLY STRAIGHT!
For real.

YANK

I CAN'T CONTROL THIS HELICOP-TER ANY-MORE!

HUH ?

WHAT DO YOU MEAN ?!

I HEAR A WEIRD NOISE TOO...
For real.

KLA NG

THE ROTOR MUST HAVE GOTTEN BUSTED BY THAT HURRICANE ATTACK...!

KLANG

142

WHERE DID Y CRASH-LAND...?!

PASSENGERS, PREPARE FOR A ROUGH LANDING...!

For real.

HEY! I'VE FOUND THE PERFECT SPOT FOR AN EMERGENCY LANDING!

WFFF

WFF

WFF

KE-

RRU NCH

PHEW! THAT WAS TOO CLOSE FOR COMFORT. WE ALMOST DOVE INTO THE RIVER. For real.

ARE YOU GUYS ALL RIGHT?

KE

RHY-HORN SEEMS OKAY TOO.

PROBABLY.

YES.

TO SEE THE FLIGHT PATH WE TOOK...

WHAT FOR?

SURE, MIGHT BE BROKEN THOUGH.

MAY I TAKE A LOOK AT THE FLIGHT RECORDER?

PLEASE BE ALL RIGHT!

Y...

OVER HERE!

FLETCHY!

THANKS, CROAKY!

ALL THOSE CRASH LANDINGS DURING CLASS WERE GOOD TRAINING.

...IT TOOK HER HOURS TO WAKE UP.

LOOKS LIKE YVETTE WON'T REGAIN CONSCIOUSNESS FOR A WHILE. AFTER SHAUNA WAS MIND-CONTROLLED...

BUT WHAT WERE SHE AND HER CLIQUE DOING WITH TEAM FLARE TO BEGIN WITH?!

I CAN SEE WHY TEAM FLARE WOULD CAPITALIZE ON YVETTE'S DISLIKE OF ME TO CONTROL HER...

I NEVER IMAGINED THEY'D SEND SKY TRAINER TRAINEES TO STEAL X'S RING...!

I'LL TAKE YVETTE SOMEWHERE SAFE WHERE SHE CAN GET HELP, AND THEN I'LL CATCH UP WITH X...

MAYBE TREVOR AND X CAN FIGURE IT OUT...

?!

...

WHAT SHOULD I DO?! **WHAT SHOULD I DO?!** I'VE GOT NO IDEA WHERE I AM!

I CAN'T FLY IN THIS!

OH NO! MY WING SUIT IS TORN!

ROUTE 9... SPIKES PASSAGE!

IT'S A PASSAGE FOR RHYHORN RIDERS!

WAIT... I KNOW THIS PLACE...

BUT I CAN'T WALK ALL THAT WAY.

AM-BRETTE TOWN IS IN THIS DIREC-TION.

I CAN NAVIGATE THROUGH THIS PASSAGE WITH MY EYES CLOSED!

MOM ALWAYS DRAGGED ME OUT HERE TO TRAIN WHEN I WAS LITTLE.

WSSSR WSSSR WSSSR

IF WE'RE LUCKY, MAYBE A RHYHORN RIDER WILL PASS BY...

FIND ANY-BODY, FLETCHY?

WHAT'S WRO— OH!

URK

AND THE OTHER ONE IS...

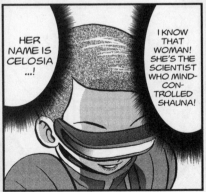
HER NAME IS CELOSIA ...!

I KNOW THAT WOMAN! SHE'S THE SCIENTIST WHO MIND-CON-TROLLED SHAUNA!

TEAM FLARE!

SHE'S A NEWS REPORT-ER!

I'VE SEEN HER ON TV!

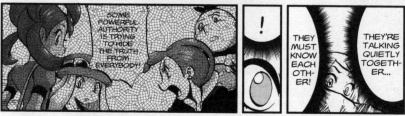

SOME POWERFUL AUTHORITY IS TRYING TO HIDE THE TRUTH FROM EVERYBODY!

!

THEY MUST KNOW EACH OTH-ER!

THEY'RE TALKING QUIETLY TOGETHER...

...CONTROLS THE MEDIA AS WELL?!

TEAM FLARE...

HAVE YOU DONE SOME SPECIAL TRAINING WITH IT?

IT'S CERTAINLY WELL TRAINED.

LADY MALVA, WHAT DID YOU THINK OF MY AEGISLASH?

THANKS FOR LENDING THIS TO ME.

SINCE THEN, I'VE BEEN CONCENTRATING ON OVERCOMING THAT WEAKNESS.

AND I DISCOVERED THAT LUCARIO'S AURA HAS THE POWER TO REPEL MIND CONTROL.

ITS MIND CONTROL WAS BROKEN MUCH SOONER THAN I EXPECTED AT SANTALUNE CITY.

...WHY I FAILED THIS MISSION!

SO, PLEASE, TELL ME...

WELL, I DON'T WANT TO MAKE THE SAME MISTAKE TWICE.

YOU ANALYZE YOUR BATTLES VERY THOROUGHLY.

AND THAT EXPERIMENT WAS A HUGE SUCCESS.

THIS MISSION WAS ACTUALLY AN EXPERIMENT WITH AEGISLASH.

BUT I DIDN'T GET RID OF THOSE CHILDREN!

ACTUALLY...

...THE FACT IS...

...YOU DIDN'T FAIL THE MISSION YOU WERE GIVEN.

YES, YOU SHOULD HAVE MORE CONFIDENCE IN YOURSELF, YOU KNOW!

IS THAT SO...?

AN... EXPERIMENT?!

...AND THAT WE CAN CONTROL FIFTEEN PEOPLE AT ONCE. SO WE'LL PROBABLY BE ABLE TO MIND CONTROL TWICE AS MANY NEXT TIME.

NOW WE HAVE PROOF THAT AEGISLASH'S MIND CONTROL CAN BE DEPLOYED OVER LONG DISTANCES...

... XERNEAS ...

WHICH MEANS... WE CAN CONTROL OUR CAPTIVES— OUR LABORERS— TO TRANS- PORT...

IT'S AN HONOR TO WORK FOR YOU.

AT ANY RATE, YOUR PERSEVERANCE AND DETERMINATION TO EXCEL IS COMMENDABLE.

... CONNECT- ED TO... THE ULTIMATE WEAPON!

...TO THE ABSORBER ...

BUT WHEN IT COMES TO DETER- MINATION... BRYONY IS THE BEST.

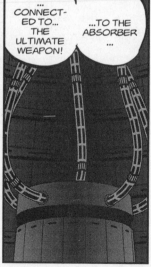

...WAS JUST AN EXPERIMENT TO SEE IF THEY COULD CONTROL MORE THAN A DOZEN PEOPLE FROM A DISTANCE ...?

THAT SKY BATTLE ...

HUH?! WHAT ARE THEY TALK-ING ABOUT ...?

I'D LOVE TO WORK WITH YOUR UNIT ON THE NEXT MISSION.

AH!

RIGHT. SOME-ONE'S UP THERE...

PSST

PSST

LADY MALVA, IT AP-PEARS THAT...

PSST

PROB-
ABLY
NO-
THING.

Psst

THANKS,
CROAKY.

Psst

THIS
IS THEIR
TERRITORY
AFTER ALL.
THERE'S A
HERD OF
THEM OVER
THERE.

MAYBE
IT WAS
JUST A
RHY-
HORN.

...AND WE PLAN TO TRANSPORT XERNEAS TONIGHT.

IN CONCLUSION, THE EXPERIMENT WAS A SUCCESS...

...BY THE TIME THE ULTIMATE WEAPON IS ACTIVATED.

...OUR BOSS DOESN'T MASTER MEGA EVOLUTION...

BUT IT WILL ALL BE FOR NAUGHT IF...

GREAT!

ALL WE NEED NOW IS THE MEGA RING!

THE BOSS ALREADY HAS A POKÉMON WHO CAN MEGA EVOLVE, AS WELL AS THE RIGHT MEGA STONE REQUIRED TO DO IT.

WE HAVE TO PREPARE EVERYTHING BY TOMORROW.

SUCH AS...?

IT CAN BE IN FORMS OTHER THAN A RING, YOU KNOW.

OR AN ACCESSORY EQUIVALENT TO THE MEGA RING...

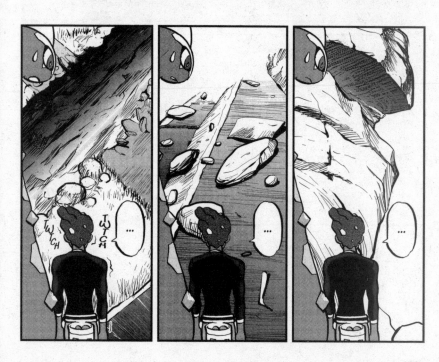

BUT HOW DO YOU PROPOSE TO GET THERE? THE CHOPPER IS HISTORY.

...Y MUST HAVE CRASH-LANDED SOME-WHERE AROUND ROUTE 9 NEAR SPIKES PASSAGE.

THERE'S NO DOUBT ABOUT IT. JUDGING FROM THE LOCATION WHERE THE HELICOPTER STARTED TO SPIN OUT AND THE SCENERY I SAW THERE...

HUH? WHAT?

HELLO. HOW'S IT GOING?

WAIT... MAYBE I CAN SUMMON MY CAR!

THAT'S NOT IMPORTANT RIGHT NOW THOUGH. I...

THIS ISN'T THE FIRST TIME...

HEY!

OH NO! EMMA HAS DISAPPEARED?

HEY!

WILL YOU SHUT UP?! CAN'T YOU SEE I'M TALKING?!

HEY!

I'M IN CHARGE OF THE CYCLING AND BOULDERING COURSE IN THIS AREA!

WHAT WAS THAT FOR?!

WHAT DO YOU MEAN YOU DIDN'T HAVE A CHOICE?!

OH, UH, SORRY... IT'S NOT LIKE WE HAD A CHOICE. For real.

AND I WANT AN EXPLANATION FOR THIS MESS!

"...LEAVE YOUR FRIENDS." REMEMBER? THE FIVE OF US ALWAYS HAVE TO STAY TOGETHER.

"DON'T...

THE GROWN-UPS CAN HANDLE THIS. WE HAVE TO START LOOKING FOR Y AS SOON AS WE CAN.

LET'S GO.

RIGHT. WAIT FOR ME!

WHAT? BUT...

EXPLA-
NATION
FIRST!

Dear Cassius,

Thank you for
to Cyllage
ve gone to lo
Y. We'll come
ack as soon as we
find her.

Trevor

I
TOLD YOU,
I'LL EXPLAIN
EVERYTHING
AFTER YOU
HAND BACK
MY HOLO
CASTER!

For
real.

YOU
HAVEN'T
SAID A
THING.

WHAT'S
WRONG,
TIERNO?
SHAUNA?

I HOPE
Y STAYED
PUT WHERE
SHE
LANDED...

IT'S
START-
ING
TO GET
DARK.

SHAUNA
AND I
HAVE
BEEN
TALKING
IT OVER,
AND...

TREVS,
X... GOT A
MINUTE?

...

S
U
R
E
!

...THAT Y HAS ALWAYS BEEN OUR LEADER.

AND THAT'S WHEN I REALIZED...

WE'VE KNOWN EACH OTHER AS FAR BACK AS I CAN REMEMBER... BUT WE'VE NEVER SEEN HER LIKE THIS BEFORE.

YOU SAW HOW DEPRESSED Y-EY WAS, RIGHT?

WE CAN'T DECIDE ON OUR NEXT MOVE.

...WE'RE HAVING TROUBLE WORKING AS A TEAM.

WITHOUT HER...

BUT DEEP INSIDE... SHE JUST COULDN'T TAKE IT ANYMORE.

Y-EY'S TOUGH. SHE NEVER COMPLAINS.

SHE PULLED HERSELF TOGETHER FOR THE BATTLE, BUT WHO KNOWS WHEN SHE'LL FALL INTO A DEPRESSION AGAIN!

EVER SINCE OUR JOURNEY BEGAN— NO, PROBABLY EVEN BEFORE THAT—WE'VE ALWAYS RELIED ON Y...WITHOUT EVEN REALIZING IT.

WE SHOULD START MAKING OUR OWN DECISIONS— TOGETHER.

FOR STARTERS...

FROM NOW ON, I THINK WE SHOULDN'T LEAN ON Y ALL THE TIME.

162

...AND RAID IT!

...WE FIND THE ENEMY'S HEAD-QUARTERS...

...I PROPOSE...

I UNDERSTAND HOW YOU FEEL, BUT...

THAT'S WHAT I PROPOSE WE DO—AS SOON AS WE MEET UP WITH Y.

IT'S TIME WE TURNED THE TABLES ON THEM!

THEY'RE ALWAYS CHASING US AND WE'RE ALWAYS RUNNING AWAY...

W...

WHAT?!

...

X! WHAT DO YOU THINK?!

SURE. WHY NOT?

⊕ **Current Location**

**Cyllage City**

A city nestled between the cliffs and the sea, overlooked by steep Bicycle racecourses.

**Route 8
Muraille Coast**

This is a road of great contrasts, from the harsh rock of the cliffs to the soft sands of the beach.

# Adventure #25
## Gathering Klefki

**X Y**

OW ...

HE WOKE UP!

GOOD MORNING, OH GREAT KALOS INVENTOR ...

... CLEMONT.

THE BAD GUYS Y AND HER FRIENDS WERE TALKING ABOUT!

TEAM FLARE ...?

REMOTE BUTTON ON!

THE HEAD-QUAR-TERS OF TEAM FLARE.

W-WHERE AM I...?!

I'VE GOT YOUR POKÉMON AND YOUR LUGGAGE.

OWW...

KLTRR KLTTR

DO AS... YOU SAY?!

I WON'T HURT YOUR POKÉMON AS LONG AS YOU DO AS I SAY.

BUT HAVE NO FEAR.

...AS-SEM-BLE THIS.

THAT'S RIGHT. I NEED YOU TO...

WHAT AN AMAZING MACHINE!

...

...I DON'T SEE WHY YOU NEED TO FORCE ME TO PUT IT TOGETHER FOR YOU!

IF YOU CAN DESIGN AN AMAZING MACHINE LIKE THAT...

THEN YOU CAN ASSEMBLE IT YOURSELF!

WHY I DID, OF COURSE.

WHO DESIGNED THIS?

I'M NOT GIVING YOU A CHOICE.

MAYBE YOU DIDN'T HEAR ME...

I'M GLAD HE DROPPED IN TO GIVE ME A HAND.

PHEW... I'M SO BUSY.

NOW GET STARTED!

YOU'LL FIND EVERYTHING YOU NEED OVER THERE.

...WHILE I CONCENTRATE ON MAKING ADJUSTMENTS TO THIS...

SHFFT

HE CAN PUT TOGETHER THAT MACHINE FOR ME...

HOW DOES THE EXPANSION SUIT FEEL?

KL NCH

BET-TER...

...THAN LAST TIME.

VERY GOOD. I'VE ADDED A COUPLE NEW FEATURES TO IT THAT I'D LIKE YOU TO TEST ONE BY ONE. FIRST, FLEX YOUR MUSCLES...

...ES-SEN-TIA.

IT'S QUIET...

...

TOO QUI-ET.

...BUT THEY HAVEN'T SHOWN UP YET TODAY.

THE GUARDS USED TO COME CHECK ON US THREE TIMES A DAY...

STRANGE...

...THIS IS OUR CHANCE... GRACE!

MAYBE...

WHAT ?!

WAIT...

OUR CHANCE TO MAKE A SIXTH ESCAPE AT-TEMPT!

WE JUST ASSUMED WE'D NEVER BE ABLE TO GET OUT OF HERE.

WE'VE BEEN TOO APATHETIC UP TILL NOW.

YEAH!

YES!

WOW, YOU WANT TO ESCAPE TOO?!

"DON'T GIVE UP! WE'LL GET OUT OF THIS PLACE TOGETHER AND RETURN TO OUR HOMETOWN!"

BUT AFTER YOUR FIFTH ESCAPE ATTEMPT, YOU TOLD US...

I SEE.

WE WERE JUST DISCUSSING THAT...

WE MIGHT AS WELL TRY TO ESCAPE FROM THIS JAIL LIKE YOU DID, GRACE.

INSTEAD OF QUIVERING WITH FEAR HERE...

WHO KNOWS WHAT HAPPENED TO THEM!

FIFTEEN PEOPLE WERE TAKEN OUT OF HERE YESTERDAY, BUT THEY HAVEN'T RETURNED...

THE SAME THING MIGHT HAPPEN TO US AT ANY MOMENT!

172

173

IT'S USUALLY SLEEPING IN THE VENT, SO THE GUARDS HAVEN'T NOTICED IT.

IT'S PROBABLY A WILD POKÉMON THAT LIVES IN THIS DUNGEON.

THOSE ARE ALL KEYS!

I WONDERED WHAT WAS DANGLING OFF OF IT WHEN I SAW IT FOR THE FIRST TIME...

LOOK!

THAT'S RIGHT!

DON'T TELL ME... YOU BEFRIENDED THIS POKÉMON... AND IT HELPED YOU ESCAPE...!

...I THOUGHT THAT MAYBE, JUST MAYBE, IT MIGHT HAVE THE KEY TO MY CELL...

IT GATHERED SO MANY KEYS...

AND **THIS** POKÉMON GATHERS KEYS FROM ALL OVER THE PLACE!

BURMY GATHERS PLANTS, SAND AND TRASH TO CREATE ITS CLOAK...

DEDENNE GATHERS BERRIES ...

...SO I ASKED THE POKÉMON TO GET ALL THE NEW KEYS IT COULD FIND FOR ME.

AND THE FIRST TIME, IT **DID** HAVE THAT KEY! THE GUARDS CHANGED THE LOCKS, THOUGH, AND ADDED MORE AFTER MY SECOND ATTEMPT...

THEN IT SHOULD STILL HAVE THE KEY I USED THE FIRST TIME! THAT KEY SHOULD FIT EVERYBODY ELSE'S CELL, AT LEAST.

THAT'S KLEFKI, THE KEY RING POKÉMON! IT NEVER LETS GO OF THE KEYS IT'S GATHERED!

BEFORE THE GUARDS COME!

GO, KLEFKI!

JINGL JINGL

Route 9
Spikes Passage

AND THIS CROSS SECTION IS STILL FRESH.

THIS ROCK DIDN'T BREAK APART NATU- RALLY...

WHERE DID Y GO?!

SHE'S NOT HERE...

IT'S AS IF... A BATTLE TOOK PLACE HERE JUST MOMENTS AGO...

HMPH!

DON'T WOR- RY US!

A BAT- TLE ...!

MAYBE THERE'S SOME-THING HERE THAT IT WANTS ...?

IT'S BEEN EXCITED EVER SINCE WE GOT ONTO THIS MOUNTAIN PATH.

HEY, CALM DOWN, RHYHORN!

SNRRt

I SEE SOMEONE!

I FOUND HER!

I GET IT. THIS IS A SPECIAL PATH FOR RHYHORN RACERS.

IT'S A RHYHORN RACER.

OH!

THAT'S WHY YOU'RE SO EXCITED. YOU'RE READY TO TRAIN, AREN'T YOU?

YOU MUST HAVE COME HERE BEFORE WITH Y.

THIS IS YVETTE, THE GIRL Y FOUGHT IN THAT SKY BATTLE!

NO!

STOP, STOP!

EX-CUSE ME!

YOU KNOW HER? GREAT!

HRM...

SHE RAN OFF. SEEMED TO BE IN AN AWFUL HURRY...

WHERE DID THAT TRAIN-ER GIRL GO?

A SKY TRAINER GIRL TOLD ME TO TAKE CARE OF HER JUST A MOMENT AGO.

178

IT'S A PEBBLE WRAPPED IN FRUBBLES...

X-EY!

I GUESS WRAPPING THE PEBBLES MAKES IT HARDER FOR THEIR OPPONENT TO SPOT THEM.

THEY COAT PEBBLES IN FRUBBLES TO THROW THEM...

THIS IS CHARACTER-ISTIC OF FROGADIER, THE EVOLVED FORM OF FROAKIE.

I READ ABOUT THIS IN A MAGA-ZINE ONCE.

PROB-ABLY...

YOU THINK CROAKY DROPPED THEM...ON PURPOSE?

THERE'S ANOTHER FRUBBLE-COATED PEBBLE DROPPED ON THE GROUND—OR MORE LIKELY, PLACED ON THE GROUND—EVERY FEW FEET OR SO!

BUT THIS ISN'T THE ONLY PEBBLE I FOUND...

SO SHE LEFT YVETTE WITH SOMEONE WHO SEEMED TRUSTWORTHY...

AFTER THAT, SHE HAD TO GO FOR SOME REASON...

AND HER FROAKIE EVOLVED INTO A FROGADIER DURING THE BATTLE.

Y MET AND FOUGHT THE ENEMY OVER THERE.

...HOPING WE'D FOLLOW HER.

...AND LEFT THIS TRAIL BEHIND...

UH... WHAT ABOUT THIS GIRL?!

OKAY, LET'S GO THEN!

SO IF WE KEEP FOLLOWING THIS TRAIL OF PEBBLES, WE'LL CATCH UP WITH Y EVENTUALLY...?

IT'S NOT LIKE Y-EY TO USE HER HEAD SO MUCH...

THAT'S RIGHT.

THANK YOU VERY MUCH!

COULD YOU TAKE HER TO A FIRST AID STATION, PLEASE?

HUH ?!

PLIP

FLOOB

IT'S SO NEAR TO THEM, BUT THEY HAVEN'T NOTICED IT.

CROAKY IS AMAZ-ING!

...SO I CAN KEEP FOLLOWING THEM FROM A DISTANCE.

AND ON TOP OF THAT, IT'S LEADING ME WITH PEBBLES WRAPPED IN ITS FRUBBLES...

I HOPE X AND THE OTHERS FOLLOW THIS TRAIL TOO.

THEY'RE PLANNING TO TRANSPORT XERNEAS...

...THIS VERY NIGHT!

...I COULDN'T JUST STAY THERE AFTER HEARING WHAT THEY WERE TALKING ABOUT.

ANY-HOW...

I HAVE TO STOP THEM!

THAT COULD CAUSE ANOTHER TRAGEDY LIKE THE ONE IN VANIVILLE TOWN!

....!

HERE.

...THE FOREST LOCATED ABOVE ROUTE 9 ON THE CLIFF BY THE MOUNTAIN...

THIS IS...

THAT'S RIGHT. I'M COUNTING ON YOU, CELOSIA.

I NEED TO GO BACK AND RETURN WITH THIRTY LABORERS, CORRECT?

YES. BUT I WAS DEFEATED.

YOU FOUGHT AGAINST KORRINA ONCE, DIDN'T YOU?

THE SUCCESSORS OF MEGA EVOLUTION...

I'LL DEAL WITH THE TRAINERS FROM SHALOUR CITY.

...IS ONE OF THEM.

THE CURRENT CHAMPION OF THE POKÉMON LEAGUE, THE ACTRESS DIANTHA...

...AND PRESENTED WITH AN ACCESSORY EQUIPPED WITH A KEY STONE.

THOSE WHO HAVE MASTERED MEGA EVOLUTION AT KALOS HAVE BEEN RECOGNIZED BY GURKINN...

KORRINA'S GRANDFATHER GURKINN IS CONSIDERED TO BE THE GURU OF MEGA EVOLUTION.

...AND THEY'RE STILL ON THE RUN.

DIANTHA JOINED THEM...

BUT GURKINN AND KORRINA DESTROYED THE TOWER OF MASTERY AND ESCAPED!

I ORDERED XEROSIC TO ABDUCT GURKINN AND MAKE HIM TEACH OUR BOSS HOW TO MASTER MEGA EVOLUTION.

RIGHT. AND I HAVE A PLAN... TO CAPTURE THEM ALL.

BOM

SO THOSE THREE ARE OUR TARGET?

...TO KNOCK THEM DOWN TO SIZE.

I CAN'T WAIT...

KRACKL

KRACKL

Y-EY!

HAVE THEY GONE, CROAKY?

HI, EVERY-ONE!

TMP

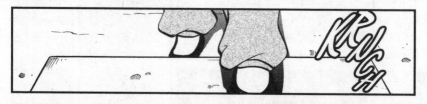

WE'LL BE FREE AS SOON AS WE GET OUT OF THIS PLACE ...!!

WE'RE FREE !!

THANKS, KLEFKI!

FOLLOW ME...

DON'T LET YOUR GUARD DOWN!

WHO GAVE THE ORDER TO LET THEM OUT OF THEIR CELLS?

WHAT'S THIS?

SH FFT

SHT O ING

OKAY, LET'S GO...

TO BE CONTINUED

# ILLUSTRATION COLLECTION

Presenting title page illustrations
originally drawn for some of the
chapters of *Pokémon Adventures: X·Y*
when they were first published in
Japanese children's magazines *Pokémon
Fan Magazine* and *Coro Coro Ichiban!*

Adventure 19, *Coro Coro Ichiban!*, December 2014 Issue

Adventure 25, *Coro Coro Ichiban!*, April 2015 Issue